Mukambu
of Ndongo

Written by Patricia Procopi
Designed and illustrated by Ruby Gardner

While this book is a work of fiction,
it is based on historical fact. In 1619
the first recorded Africans arrived at
Jamestown, Virginia. Our story tells the
tale of a young West Central African girl,
kidnapped from her home, who arrived
with that first group. As she thinks back
on her life, she tells her granddaughter
about her life in Africa, her arrival in
Virginia and the life she lived
in this strange new world.

"Grandma? Are you alright? Can I get you anything?"

"No, child. I was just asleep ... dreaming here by the fire. I have lived most of my years in this place, but I find each year the winters are harder and harder. When I sit by this hot fire and fall asleep, I dream I am back in the land where I was born, where it was hot all the time."

"Where were you born Grandma?"

"Why child, in Africa."

"Africa? Tell me about it, Grandma."

"When I was young, about your age, I lived in a village in a land far, far away from here, a place called Ndongo, across the sea. Then I was called 'Mukambu.' I lived with my mother and father, my brothers and sisters, and all my people in the same village. The land was rich, and my mother and my sisters and I would work in our fields each day planting and harvesting. My father was an important man in the village. He owned many goats and cattle. I was at the age when young men began to look at me and think about marriage. My father had many goats for my dowry.

"I was happy then. We had everything we needed, a good home and plenty to eat. I thought I would live there the rest of my life with my family and start a family of my own. But fear began to creep into our village and our lives. Rumors came from other villages about men who came from the west, who would attack villages and capture the people of the village and march them away, never to be seen again. I tried not to worry. It didn't seem possible.

"But one day when my mother and I were returning from the fields, we heard shouting and screams from the village. We ran towards the village and saw the houses on fire and people running. We tried to run, but men came out of the jungle and grabbed us. They caught all the people they could and tied us together in a long line. Then they began to march us away from the village. That night I began to cry, but my mother told me not to. She said our people were brave and would never show fear to the enemy. I wiped away my tears.

"The next morning when we woke up, my mother and I looked for anyone else from my family in the line, but there was no one. We hoped the rest had escaped. We marched for days. I lost time. We were hungry and tired. Each day all I thought about was marching.

"One day, we arrived in a large city by the sea. It was the first time I had seen so many people living in one place. I didn't like it. It was noisy and dirty. We were taken to a place by the water. I had never seen so much water. It went to the bottom of the sky.

"There were hundreds of people crowded into pens like animals. We stayed there for days. We had little food or water. We learned that we were going to be put on boats and taken to another land across the ocean where we would no longer be free but would work in fields for other people. My heart sank to think I would leave everything I knew and that all my dreams for my life were gone.

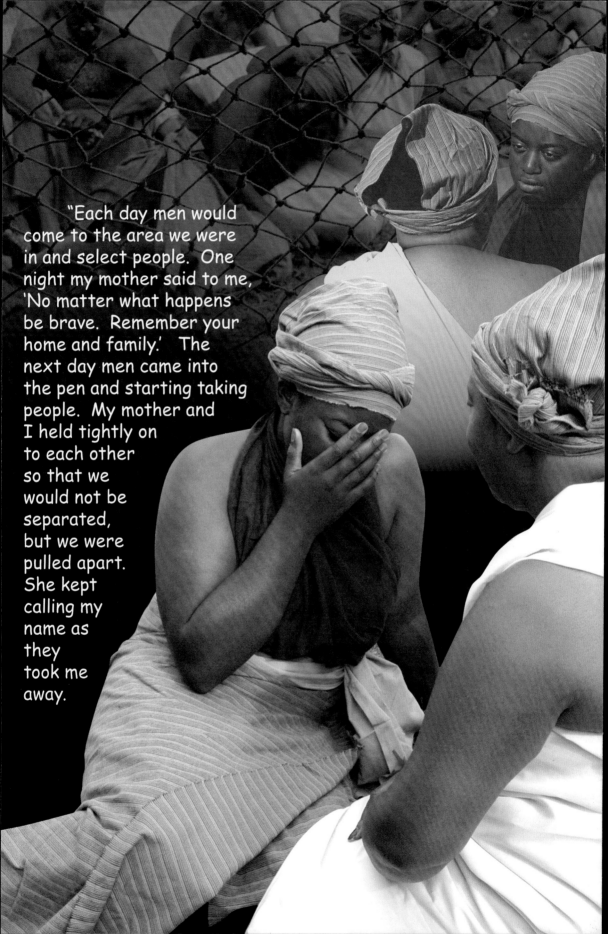

"Each day men would come to the area we were in and select people. One night my mother said to me, 'No matter what happens be brave. Remember your home and family.' The next day men came into the pen and starting taking people. My mother and I held tightly on to each other so that we would not be separated, but we were pulled apart. She kept calling my name as they took me away.

"Those of us who were taken out of the pen were taken to a beach. We were lined up, and a Portuguese priest walked by, asking each of us if we had been baptized. I told him no, and he made a sign on my forehead and told me I was now to be called by my Christian name 'Lucretia.' I had lost one more part of my home. We were then put on a small boat and taken out to a ship.

"We were put in the bottom of the ship, and the opening to the outside was closed on us. I thought I had seen the sun for the last time. It was dark and hot and terrible. I shut my mind to it and dreamed I was back at my home. I did not cry.

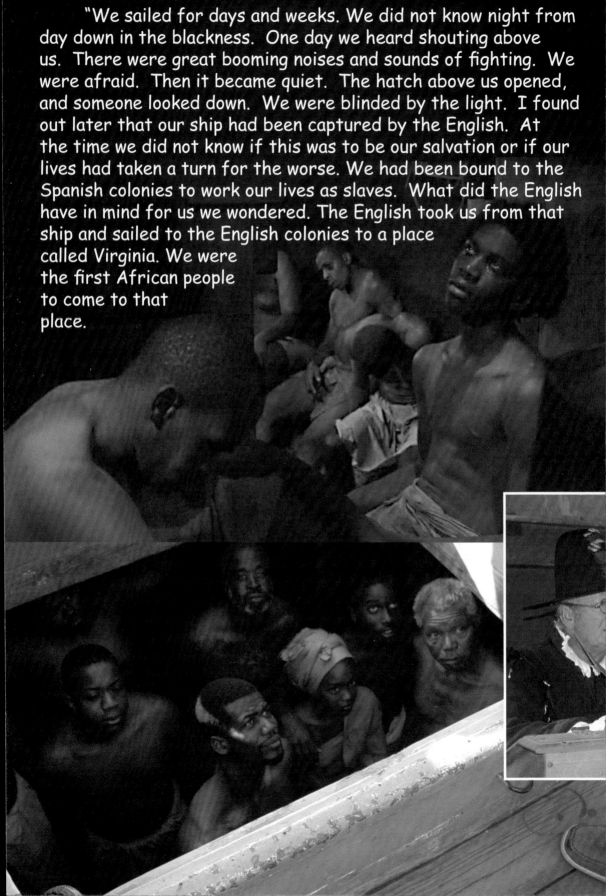

"We sailed for days and weeks. We did not know night from day down in the blackness. One day we heard shouting above us. There were great booming noises and sounds of fighting. We were afraid. Then it became quiet. The hatch above us opened, and someone looked down. We were blinded by the light. I found out later that our ship had been captured by the English. At the time we did not know if this was to be our salvation or if our lives had taken a turn for the worse. We had been bound to the Spanish colonies to work our lives as slaves. What did the English have in mind for us we wondered. The English took us from that ship and sailed to the English colonies to a place called Virginia. We were the first African people to come to that place.

"When we landed at a place called Point Comfort, the sailors traded about 20 of us for food. I was in that group. They sailed away, and we were taken up river to the main English town called Jamestown. There we were divided up and sent to work in the houses of the Governor of Virginia and the Cape Merchant. I went to work in the house of the English Governor, George Yeardley. I helped his wife with her baby, Elizabeth.

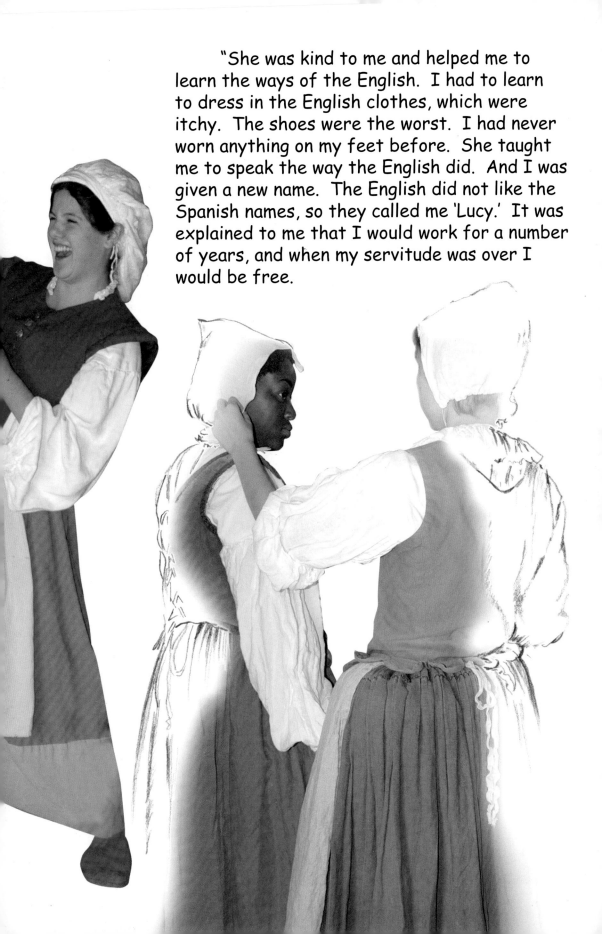

"She was kind to me and helped me to learn the ways of the English. I had to learn to dress in the English clothes, which were itchy. The shoes were the worst. I had never worn anything on my feet before. She taught me to speak the way the English did. And I was given a new name. The English did not like the Spanish names, so they called me 'Lucy.' It was explained to me that I would work for a number of years, and when my servitude was over I would be free.

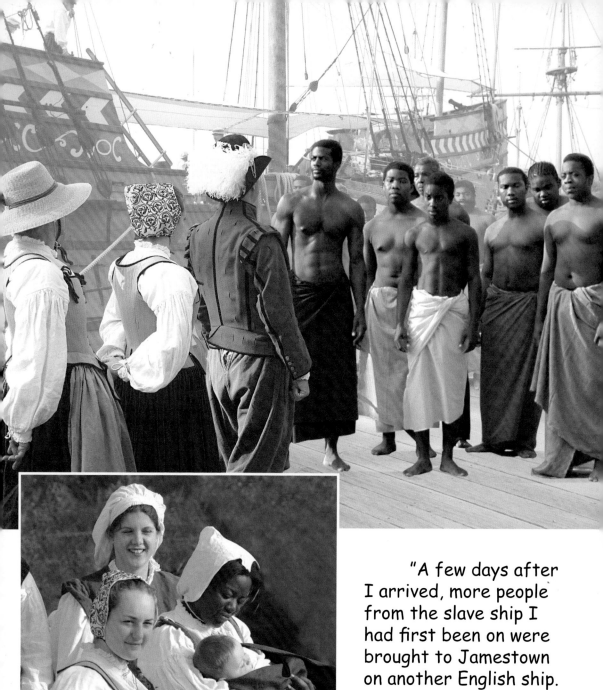

"A few days after I arrived, more people from the slave ship I had first been on were brought to Jamestown on another English ship. I went down to the docks to see them. I remembered a young man from the voyage and wondered if he was among the new arrivals. I saw him but did not speak.

"After I had been there for some months, I came up with a plan. I spoke to Mrs. Yeardley and told her I would work twice as long for her so that I could earn enough to sail back to Ndongo, go to my village and find my family. Mrs. Yeardley sadly explained to me that I could never go home again. She said I would probably just be taken and sold as a slave, and even if I was able to get back to my village, my family might be all gone. That night I cried.

"In my heart I said goodbye to my family forever. For the first time I realized that I would have to make this strange land my home.

"The land was strange and new to me, but I found out it was a strange land for the English as well. They had only been there for 12 years. The people who lived on the land before they came were called the Powhatans by the English. They were more like the people from my village. They lived with the land, not just on it like the English. They hunted and fished and planted. The English were afraid of them but needed to trade with them. The land was covered by thick forests, and the summers were hot, bu the winters were long and cold. I was not used to that

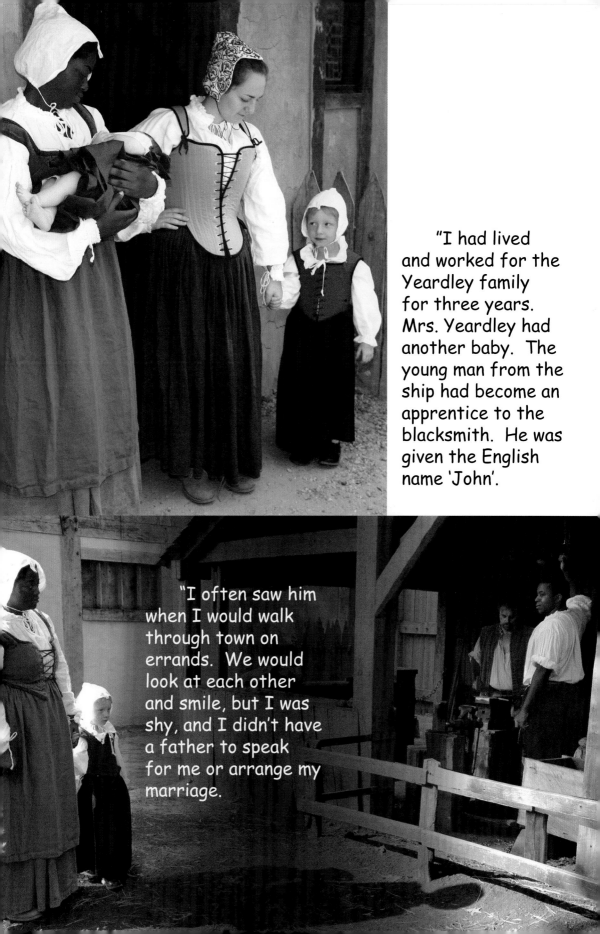

"I had lived and worked for the Yeardley family for three years. Mrs. Yeardley had another baby. The young man from the ship had become an apprentice to the blacksmith. He was given the English name 'John'.

"I often saw him when I would walk through town on errands. We would look at each other and smile, but I was shy, and I didn't have a father to speak for me or arrange my marriage.

"More people from Africa came to work in Virginia. Tobacco was being grown everywhere in the settlements along the James River, and people were needed to work in the fields. This began to feel like my home. Many different people lived and worked together in this strange new world.

"We did not know it, but the Powhatans were not happy with the English. The old chief Powhatan, the father of Pocahontas had died, and their new chief felt that the English had been stealing their land. One morning they rose up against us. I was one of the lucky ones because we lived near the James fort, but settlers in the outlying areas were attacked. Many were killed. The survivors came to the fort for protection. We had to nurse many of them that had been injured.

"The English survived this attack, but they were more afraid of the Indians than before. Many of the outlying settlements were abandoned. We saw less and less of the Indians, since they no longer came to Jamestown to trade. Life at our settlement continued about the same.

"When my years of work in the house with the Governor ended, he helped arrange my marriage with the young

blacksmith John. After we married, your grandfather and I moved away from Jamestown. We worked a small piece of land which we eventually purchased with the money we made from the tobacco we grew.

"We worked, we had children, including your mother, and we thrived.

"In later times, more and more Africans were brought to Virginia, to work in the tobacco fields. They came as slaves. They couldn't work for their freedom like we had. But we were always free. That is what I want you to remember, child, we were always free."

GLOSSARY

Blacksmith - A person who creates objects from iron by forging the metal using tools to hammer, bend, cut or otherwise shape it. Among the first colonists at Jamestown was a blacksmith who repaired metal tools. The African people of Ndongo were familiar with blacksmithing.

Baptism - A Christian sacrament in which a person is ritually cleansed with water and becomes a member of the Christian church. The Portuguese Roman Catholic priests baptized all of the Africans they captured and gave them Christian names. If the slaves then perished on the journey to the New World, this would ensure that their souls would be saved.

Cape Merchant - The cape merchant in the early Virginia colony was the officer in charge of the storehouses and oversaw all supplies coming into Virginia and all goods being shipped out to England. At the time of the arrival of the first recorded Africans in the colony, the cape merchant had evolved into the person who exchanged goods in the Virginia Company storehouses for what was being produced by the settlers on private plantations, particularly tobacco and sassafras.

Dowry - The money, goods or land that a woman brought to her husband in marriage. Dowries were usually negotiated between the families of the bride and groom.

Governor Yeardley - Sir George Yeardley (1587-1627) was a plantation owner and governor of the Virginia colony. He was a passenger on the Third Supply fleet's flagship, Sea Venture, which shipwrecked in Bermuda. He arrived in Virginia from Bermuda in May 1610. In 1613 Yeardley married Temperance Flowerdew, who had been on another ship in the Third Supply and had arrived in Virginia in 1609. Temperance was a survivor of the starving winter of 1609-10. Yeardley was knighted in 1618 and was commissioned Governor of Virginia. The Yeardleys had three children, Elizabeth, Argoll and Francis.

Indentured Servant - A laborer who is under contract to an employer for a certain period of time, usually three to seven years. The servant's labor was in exchange for transportation, food, clothing, lodging and other necessities. Unlike a slave, an indentured servant was required to work only for a limited term specified in a signed contract.

Ndongo - An African kingdom in West Central Africa and the homeland of the first recorded Africans who were brought to Virginia. The Portuguese took over part of the territory and created the Portuguese colony of Angola.

Point Comfort - An area established by the English in 1607 at the mouth of the James River. The English established a small garrison there to watch for an attack from the

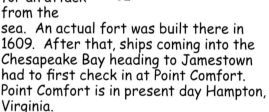

sea. An actual fort was built there in 1609. After that, ships coming into the Chesapeake Bay heading to Jamestown had to first check in at Point Comfort. Point Comfort is in present day Hampton, Virginia.

Portugal - A country which, with Spain, was one of the two major colonizing forces at the beginning of the Age of Discovery. Portugal sent explorers south and east around Africa, claiming land along the coast. In the mid-16th century, Portugal claimed

West Central Africa and created its colony of Angola which included the African kingdom of Ndongo.

Powhatan - Wahunsonacock, known as Powhatan, was the supreme ruler of the Indian tribes in Tidewater Virginia. Best known as the father of Pocahontas, Powhatan forged a tenuous trade relationship with the English settlers. Powhatan died in 1618 and was succeeded by his younger brother, Opechancanough, who attempted to drive the English from his lands in 1622. This war resulted in the deaths of almost a third of the English settlers and led to ten years of intermittent warfare before peace was declared.

Powhatan Indians - At the time of the English arrival in the Chesapeake area in 1607, approximately 32 tribes consisting of about 14,000 Indians were living in Virginia's coastal plain.

Privateer - A private warship authorized by a country, city or individual through a letter of marque giving the ship permission to attack foreign shipping. English privateers working under such situations cruised the Caribbean and off the coast of Spain, trying to intercept treasure ships coming from the Spanish Main. Privateers were entitled to attack only during wartime; however states often encouraged raids on ships of other countries in times of peace as well.

Slavery - The labor condition in which people were owned by others as property, usually for their lifetime. Slavery in the New World began when the Spanish enslaved the native Indian populations of the lands they conquered. In the 16th century the Spanish contracted with the Portuguese to transport slaves from the Portuguese colonies in Africa to the Spanish colonies in the New World. In 1619 the first recorded Africans arrived at Jamestown. Privateers captured them from a Portuguese slave ship en route to Veracruz, Mexico. At the time there were no laws regarding slavery in Virginia; slave laws were not passed in the English colony until the 1660s. The 1619 Africans were most likely treated as servants to the English.

Tenant Farmer - Someone who farms a tract of land for a landlord. In 17th-century Virginia, tenant farmers often were former servants who worked off their period of servitude but did not own any land. Depending on the arrangement, the tenant paid the owner a portion of the crops or cash that he would make on the land he farmed in a year. In some cases the farmer could earn or buy the ownership of the land after a number of years.

Tobacco - John Rolfe, the husband of Pocahontas, planted the first sweet-scented tobacco seeds in Virginia, a type which the English found more pleasing than the bitter native tobacco planted by the Virginia Indians. By 1614 the first shipment of Virginia tobacco was sold in London. Soon tobacco became the rage and everyone was growing this cash crop. Tobacco saved the Jamestown colony, but it also used up the land and created the need for a huge labor force. This eventually led to the institution of slavery in America.

FOR FURTHER READING

If you would like to learn more about the Africans, English settlers and Powhatan Indians, we suggest the following titles:

CHILDREN'S BOOKS

Anne of Jamestown
by Anne Price-Hardister
Jamestown-Yorktown Foundation,
Bicast Publishing

Eyewitness Books – Africa
by Yvonne Ayo
Dorling Kindersley

Exploring Angola: A Young Person's Guide by Linda C. Goss
Maya Publications

The Jamestown Colony (Let Freedom Ring) by Gayle Worland
Capstone Press

Nzingha, Warrior Queen of Matamba: Angola, 1595 by Patricia McKissack
Scholastic Books

The Slave Trade in Early America by Kristin Thoennes Keller
Capstone Press

William: Ships Boy by Frances Norton Honich
Jamestown-Yorktown Foundation,
Bicast Publishing

Winganusk of the Powhatans
by Janet Gallagher
Jamestown-Yorktown Foundation,
Bicast Publishing

ADULT BOOKS

Birth of Black America: The First African-Americans and the Pursuit of Freedom at Jamestown by Tim Hashaw
Publishers Group West

Captive Passage: The Transatlantic Slave Trade
Mariner's Museum/Smithsonian Press

Central Africans, Atlantic Creoles, and the Foundation of the Americas 1585-1660 by Linda M. Heywood and John K. Thornton
Cambridge University Press

Jamestown Settlement: A Pictorial Guide by Nancy Egloff
Jamestown-Yorktown Foundation,
Bicast Publishing

Love and Hate in Jamestown: John Smith, Pocahontas and the Heart of a New Nation by David A. Price
Random House

Many Thousands Gone: The First Two Centuries of Slavery in North America by Ira Berlin
Harvard University Press

Pocahontas and the Powhatan Dilemma by Camilla Townsend
Hill and Wang

Pocahontas's People by Helen Rountree
University of Oklahoma Press

These and many other titles are available in the Jamestown Settlement Museum Gift Shop. Call 757-253-7308 or visit us online at shophistoryisfun.com